Fifty
Favorite
Christmas
Songs
&Carols

Fifty
Favorite
Christmas
Songs
& Carols

BARNES
&NOBLE
BOOKS
NEW YORK

2000 Barnes & Noble Books

ISBN: 0-7607-2320-6

Printed and bound in the United States of America

    02 MP 9 8 7 6 5 4 3

MSC

Contents

Silent Night

Words by Joseph Mohr
(1792–1849)

Music by Franz Xaver Gruber
(1787–1863)

2. Silent night! Holy night!
   Shepherds quake at the sight!
   Glories stream from heaven afar,
   Heav'nly hosts sing Alleluia,
   Christ, the Savior, is born!
   Christ, the Savior, is born!

3. Silent night! Holy night!
   Sun of God, love's pure light,
   Radiant beams from Thy holy face,
   With the dawn of redeeming grace,
   Jesus, Lord at Thy birth,
   Jesus, Lord at Thy birth.

4. Silent night! Holy night!
   Wondrous star, lend thy light;
   With the angels let us sing
   Alleluia to our King;
   Christ, the Savior is born.
   Christ. the Savior is born.

The Moon Shines Bright

Traditional English carol

Moderato

1. The moon shines bright and the stars give light, A
2. A - wake, a - wake, good people all, A -

lit - tle be - fore the day; Our might - y Lord, He
wake, and you shall hear, The Lord our God died

looked on us And bade us a - wake and pray!
on the cross, For us He loved so dear.

It Came Upon a Midnight Clear

Words by Edmund Hamilton Sears
(1810–1876)

Music by Richard Storrs Willis
(1819–1900)

2. Still through the cloven skies they come,
   With peaceful wings unfurled,
   And still their heav'nly music floats
   O'er all the weary world;
   Above its sad and lowly plain
   They bend on hovering wing,
   And ever over its Babel sounds
   The blessèd angels sing.

3. Yet with the woes of sin and strife
   The world has suffered long;
   Beneath the angel-strain have rolled
   Two thousand years of wrong;
   And man, at war with man, hears not
   The love-song which they bring.
   O hush the noise, ye men of strife,
   And hear the angels sing.

4. And ye, beneath life's crushing load,
   Whose forms are bending low,
   Who toil along the climbing way
   With weary steps and slow:
   Look up! for glad and golden hours
   Come swiftly on the wing;
   O rest beside the weary road
   And hear the angels sing.

5. For lo! the days are hastening on,
   By prophet bards foretold,
   When with the ever-circling years
   Comes round the Age of Gold.
   When peace shall over all the earth
   Its ancient splendors fling,
   And the whole world give back the song
   Which now the angels sing.

O Little Town of Bethlehem

Words by Phillips Brooks
(1835–1893)

Music by Lewis H. Redner
(1831–1908)

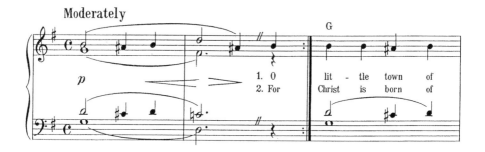

1. O lit - tle town of
2. For Christ is born of

Beth - le - hem! How still we see thee lie; A - bove thy deep and
Ma - ry, And gath - ered all a - bove, While mor - tals sleep, the

dream - less sleep The si - lent stars go by; Yet in thy dark streets
an - gels keep Their watch of won - d'ring love. O morn - ing stars, to

shin - eth The ev - er - last - ing light: The hopes and fears of
geth - er Pro - claim the ho - ly birth! And prais - es sing to

3. How silently, how silently,
   The wondrous gift is giv'n!
   So God imparts to human hearts
   The blessing of His heav'n.
   No ear may hear His coming,
   But in this world of sin,
   Where meek souls will receive Him still
   The dear Christ enters in.

4. O Holy Child of Bethlehem!
   Descend to us, we pray;
   Cast out our sin, and enter in;
   Be born in us today.
   We hear the Christmas angels
   The great glad tidings tell;
   O come to us, abide with us,
   Our Lord Emmanuel.

All My Heart This Night Rejoices

Words by Paul Gerhardt
(1607–1676)

Music by Johann G. Ebeling
(1637–1676)

All my heart this night re - joic - es,

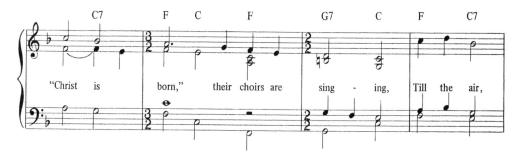

As I hear, far and near, Sweet - est an - gel voic - es:

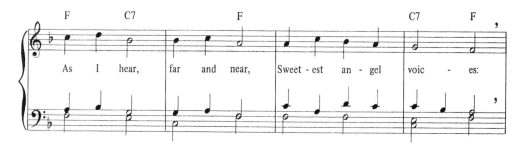

"Christ is born," their choirs are sing - ing, Till the air,

ev - 'ry - where, Now with joy is ring - ing.

2. Hark! a voice from yonder manger
   Soft and sweet, doth entreat;
   "Flee from woe and danger;
   Brethren come; from all that grieves you
   You are freed; all you need
   I will surely give you."

3. Come, then, let us hasten yonder;
   Here let all, great and small
   Kneel in awe and wonder;
   Love Him, who with love is yearning;
   Hail the star, that from far
   Bright with hope is burning!

Jolly Old St. Nicholas

Traditional Christmas song

2. When the clock is striking twelve,
   When I'm fast asleep,
   Down the chimney broad and black,
   With your pack you'll creep;
   All the stockings you will find
   Hanging in a row;
   Mine will be the shortest one,
   You'll be sure to know.

3. Johnny wants a pair of skates;
   Susy wants a dolly;
   Nelly wants a storybook;
   She thinks dolls are folly;
   As for me, my little brain
   Isn't very bright;
   Choose for me, old Santa Claus,
   What you think is right.

Up on the Housetop

Words and music by B.R. Hanby

Gaily

1. Up on the house-top the rein-deer pause, Out jumps good old San-ta Claus;

Down thro' the chim-ney with lots of toys, All for the lit-tle ones' Christ-mas joys.

Refrain

Ho, Ho, Ho! Who would-n't go! Ho, Ho, Ho! Who would-n't go!___

Up on the house-top, click, click, click, Down thro' the chim-ney with good Saint Nick.

2. First comes the stocking of little Nell;
Oh, dear Santa, fill it well;
Give her a dolly that laughs and cries,
One that will open and shut her eyes.
Refrain

3. Next comes the stocking of little Will;
Oh, just see what a glorious fill;
Here is a hammer and lots of tacks,
Also a ball and a whip that cracks.
Refrain

The First Nowell

Traditional English carol

Refrain

Now - ell,___ Now - ell, Now - ell, Now - ell,___

Born is the King___ of Is - ra - el.

3. And by the light of that same star
   Three wise men came from country far;
   To seek for a king was their intent
   And to follow the star wheresoever it went:
   Refrain

4. This star drew nigh to the northwest;
   O'er Bethlehem it took its rest.
   And there it did both stop and stay
   Right over the place where Jesus lay.
   Refrain

5. Then entered in those wise men three
   Fell reverently upon their knee,
   And offered there in His presence
   Both gold and myrrh and frankincense.
   Refrain

6. Then let us all with one accord
   Sing praises to our heavenly Lord
   That hath made heaven and earth of naught
   And with His blood mankind hath brought.
   Refrain

Angels We Have Heard on High

Traditional French carol

1. An - gels we have heard on high, Sweet-ly sing - ing on the plain.
2. Shep-herds why this ju - bi-lee? Why your joy-ful strains pro-long?

And the moun-tains in re-ply Ech - o - ing their joy - ous strain:
What the glad-some ti - dings be Which in-spire your heav' - nly song?

Refrain

Glo - - - - - - - - - ri - a

in ex - cel - sius de - o. de - o.

3. Come to Bethlehem and see
   Him whose birth the angels sing;
   Come adore on bended knee
   Christ, the Lord, the newborn King.
   Refrain

4. See Him in a manger laid,
   Whom the choir of angels priase;
   Holy Spirit lend thine aid,
   While our hearts in love we raise.
   Refrain

Hark! the Herald Angels Sing

Words by Charles Wesley
(1707–1788)

Music by Felix Mendelssohn
(1809–1847)

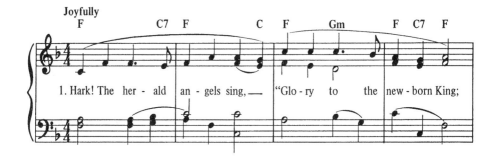

1. Hark! The her - ald an - gels sing, — "Glo - ry to the new - born King;

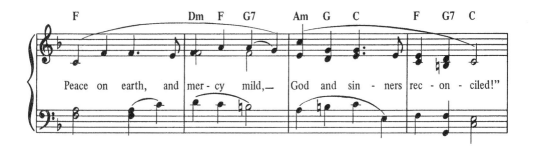

Peace on earth, and mer - cy mild, — God and sin - ners rec - on - ciled!"

Joy - ful, all ye na - tions, rise, — Join the tri - umph of the skies; —

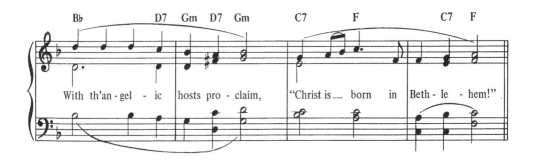

With th'an - gel - ic hosts pro - claim, "Christ is — born in Beth - le - hem!"

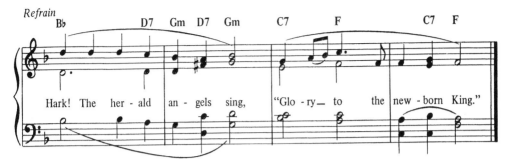

Refrain

Hark! The her - ald an - gels sing, "Glo - ry— to the new - born King."

2. Christ, by highest heaven adored;
   Christ, the everlasting Lord;
   Late in time behold Him come,
   Offspring of the Virgin's womb.
   Veiled in flesh the Godhead see;
   Hail th' Incarnate Deity,
   Pleased as man with men to dwell;
   Jesus, our Emmanuel.
   Refrain

3. Hail the heavenborn Prince of Peace!
   Hail the Sun of Righteousness!
   Light and life to all He brings,
   Risen with healing in His wings;
   Mild He lays His glory by,
   Born that man no more may die,
   Born to raise the sons of earth,
   Born to give them second birth.
   Refrain

Angels From the Realms of Glory

Words by James Montgomery
(1771–1854)

Henry Smart
(1813–1879)

With spirit

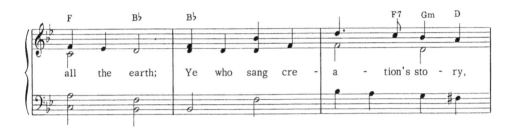

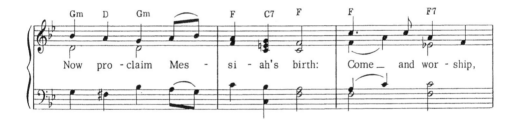

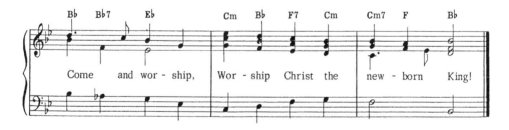

2. Shepherds, in the fields abiding,
   Watching o'er your flocks by night,
   God with man is now residing,
   Yonder shines the infant Light:
   Come and worship, Come and worship,
   Worship Christ, the newborn King!

3. Sages, leave your contemplations,
   Brighter visions beam afar;
   Seek the great Desire of nations;
   Ye have seen His natal star:
   Come and worship, Come and worship,
   Worship Christ, the newborn King!

While Shepherds Watched Their Flocks

Words by Nahum Tate
(1652–1715)

Music by George Frideric Handel
(1685–1759)

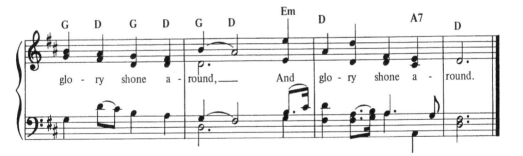

2. "Fear not!" said he, for mighty dread
   Had seized their troubled mind,
   "Glad tidings of great joy I bring,
   To you and all mankind,
     To you and all mankind.

3. "To you, in David's town, this day
   Is born of David's line
   The Savior who is Christ the Lord,
   And this shall be the sign,
     And this shall be the sign.

4. "The Heav'nly Babe you there shall find
   To human view displayed,
   All meanly wrapped in swathing band
   And in a manger laid,
     And in a manger laid.

5. "All glory be to God on high,
   And to the earth be peace,
   Good will henceforth from heav'n to men,
   Begin and never cease,
     Begin and never cease."

Rise Up, Shepherd, an' Follow

Traditional African-American spiritual

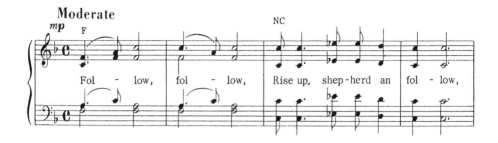

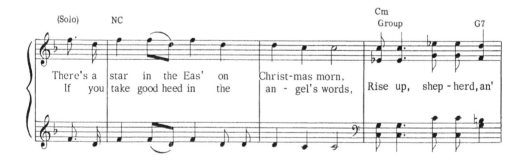

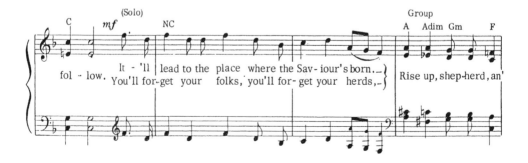

fol - low. Leave your sheep and leave your lambs, Rise up, shep-herd, an' fol - low.

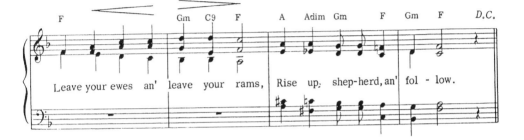

Leave your ewes an' leave your rams, Rise up, shep-herd, an' fol - low.

Bring a Torch, Jeannette, Isabella

(Un flambeau, Jeanette, Isabelle)

Traditional French carol

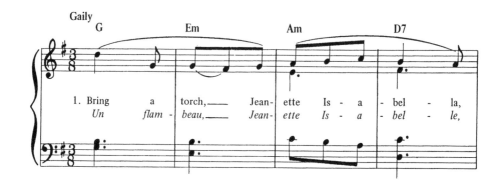

1. Bring a torch,— Jean-ette Is - a - bel - la,
Un flam - beau,— Jean-ette Is - a - bel - le,

Bring a torch to the sta - ble run!
Un flam - beau,— cou - rons au ber - ceau!

It is Je - sus, good folk of the vil - lage;
C'est Je - sus, bon - nes gens du ha - meau,—

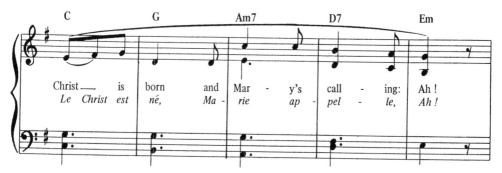

Christ— is born and Mar - y's call - ing: Ah!
Le Christ est né, Ma - rie ap - pel - le, Ah!

D   G   D   G   B7   Em

Ah !   beau - ti - ful   is   the   moth - er,   Ah !
Ah !   *que___ la   mère   est   bel - le,*   *Ah !*

D   G   D   G

Ah !   beau - ti - ful   is   her   son !___
Ah !   *ah ! que l'en - fant   est   beau !___*

2. It is wrong when the child is sleeping,
   It is wrong to talk so loud;
   Silence, all, as you gather around,
   Lest your noise should waken Jesus:
   Hush! hush! see how fast he slumbers:
   Hush! hush! see how fast he sleeps!

3. Softly to the little stable,
   Softly for a moment come;
   Look and see how charming is Jesus,
   How he is white, his cheeks are rosy!
   Hush! hush! see how the child is sleeping;
   Hush! hush! see how he smiles in his dreams.

Away in a Manger

Words Traditional

Music by James R. Murray
(1841–1905)

2. The cattle are lowing, the baby awakes,
   But little Lord Jesus, no crying he makes.
   I love thee, Lord Jesus, look down from the sky,
   And stay by my cradle till morning is nigh.

3. Be near me Lord Jesus, I ask thee to stay
   Close by me forever, and love me, I pray.
   Bless all the dear children in thy tender care,
   And fit us for heaven to live with thee there.

Joy to the World

Words by Isaac Watts
(1674–1748)

Traditional English
tune: 'Antioch'

2. Joy to the world! The Savior reigns;
   Let men their songs employ;
   While fields and floods, rocks, hills and plains
   Repeat the sounding joy,
   Repeat the sounding joy,
   Repeat, repeat the sounding joy.

3. He rules the world with truth and grace,
   And makes the nations prove
   The glories of His righteousness,
   And wonders of His love,
   And wonders of His love,
   And wonders, wonders of His love.

What Child Is This?

Words by William Chatterton Dix
(1837–1898)

Traditional English air:
'Greensleeves'

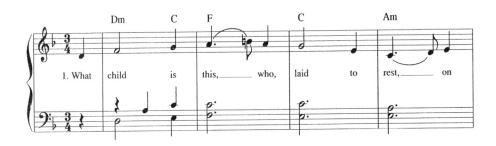

1. What child is this, who, laid to rest, on

Ma — ry's lap is sleep — ing? Whom

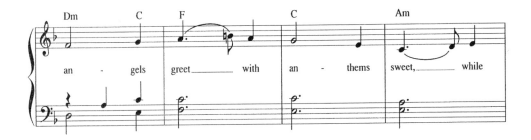

an — gels greet with an — thems sweet, while

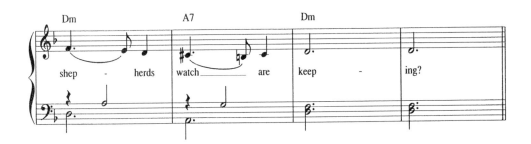

shep — herds watch are keep — ing?

Refrain

This, this_____ is Christ the King,_____ whom shep - herds guard_____ and an - gels sing. Haste, haste_____ to bring Him laud,_____ the Babe,_____ the Son_____ of Ma - ry.

2. Why lies He in such mean estate
Where ox and ass are feeding?
Good Christian, fear: for sinners here
The silent Word is pleading.
Refrain

3. So bring Him incense, gold, and myrrh
Come peasant, king, to own Him
The King of Kings salvation brings
Let loving hearts enthrone Him.
Refrain

Coventry Carol

Traditional English carol

Refrain

p Lul - ly, lul - la, thou lit - tle ti - ny

Child. By, by, lul - ly, lul - lay.

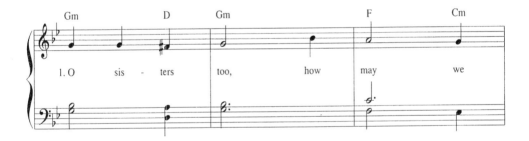

1. O sis - ters too, how may we

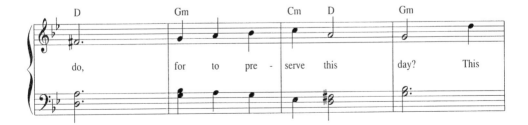

do, for to pre - serve this day? This

poor young - ling, for whom we do sing, by, by, lul - ly, lul - lay.

2. Herod the king in his raging,
   Chargèd he hath this day
   His men of might, in his own sight,
   All children young to slay.
   Refrain

3. That woe is me, poor Child, for Thee,
   And ever mourn and say,
   For Thy parting nor say nor sing,
   By, by lully, lullay.
   Refrain

Infant Holy, Infant Lowly

Traditional Polish carol

2. Flocks were sleeping, shepherds keeping
   Vigil till the morning new,
   Saw the glory, heard the story,
   Tidings of a gospel true.
   Thus rejoicing, free from sorrow,
   Praises voicing, greet the morrow,
   Christ the babe was born for you,
   Christ the babe was born for you.

The Friendly Beasts

Traditional English carol

3. "I," said the cow, all white and red,
   "I have Him my manger for his bed.
   I gave Him hay to pillow his head."
   "I," said the cow, all white and red.

4. "I," said the sheep, with curly horn,
   "I gave Him my wool for his blanket warm;
   He wore my coat on Christmas morn."
   "I," said the sheep, with curly horn.

5. "I," said the dove, from rafters high,
   "Cooed Him to sleep that He should not cry;
   We cooed Him to sleep, my mate and I."
   "I," said the dove, from rafters high.

6. Thus every beast by some good spell
   In the stable dark was glad to tell
   Of the gift he gave Emmanuel,
   The gift he gave Emmanuel.

Joseph Dearest, Joseph Mine

Traditional German carol

Jo — seph, dear — est Jo — seph mine Help me cra — dle the

child di — vine; God re — ward thee and all that's thine In

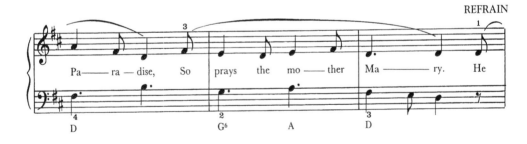

REFRAIN

Pa — ra — dise, So prays the mo — ther Ma — ry. He

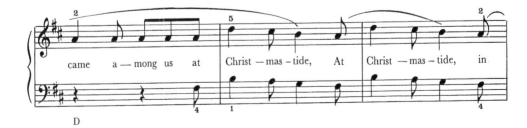

came a — mong us at Christ — mas — tide, At Christ — mas — tide, in

Beth——le——hem; Men shall bring Him from far and wide Love's

Esus E A D

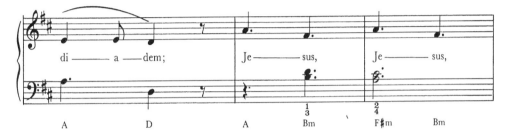

di————a——dem; Je————sus, Je————sus,

A D A Bm F#m Bm

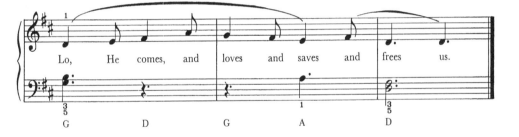

Lo, He comes, and loves and saves and frees us.

G D G A D

2. Gladly, dear one, lady mine,
   Help I cradle this child of thine;
   God's own light on us both shall shine
   In Paradise,
   As prays the mother Mary.
   Refrain

3. Peace to all that have goodwill,
   God who heaven and earth doth fill,
   Comes to turn us away from ill,
   And lies so still
   Within the crib of Mary.
   Refrain

4. All shall come and bow the knee,
   Wise and happy their souls shall be,
   Loving such a divinity,
   As all may see
   In Jesus, son of Mary.
   Refrain

5. Now is born Emmanuel,
   Prophesied once by Ezekiel,
   Promised Mary by Gabriel—
   Ah, who can tell
   Thy praises, son of Mary.
   Refrain

6. Thou my lazy heart has stirred,
   Thou, the Father's eternal word,
   Greater than aught that ear hath heard,
   Thou tiny bird
   Of love, thou son of Mary.
   Refrain

Mary Had a Boychild

Traditional West Indian carol

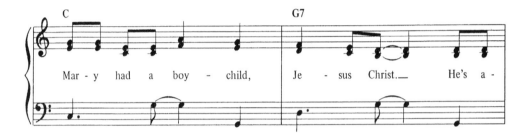

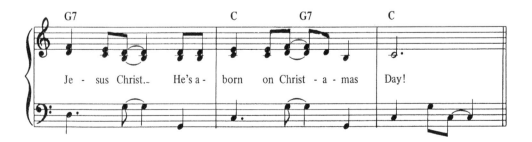

Verse

Long time a - go in Beth - le - hem,— so the

Ho - ly Bi - ble say, Mar - y's boy - child

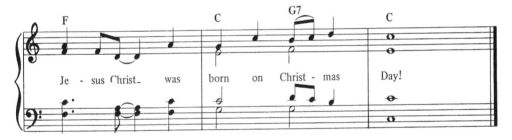

Je - sus Christ— was born on Christ - mas Day!

As With Gladness Men of Old

Words by William Chatterton Dix
(1837–1898)

Music by Konrad Kocher
(1786–1872)

1. As with gladness men of old Did the guiding star behold; As with joy they hail'd its light, Leading onward, beaming bright. So most gracious Lord, may we Evermore be led by thee.

2. As with joyful steps they sped To that lowly manger bed, There to bend the knee before Him who heav'n and earth adore, So may we with willing feet Ever seek Thy mercy seat.

Dona Nobis Pacem

Traditional German carol

We Three Kings of Orient Are

Words and music by John Henry Hopkins
(1820–1891)

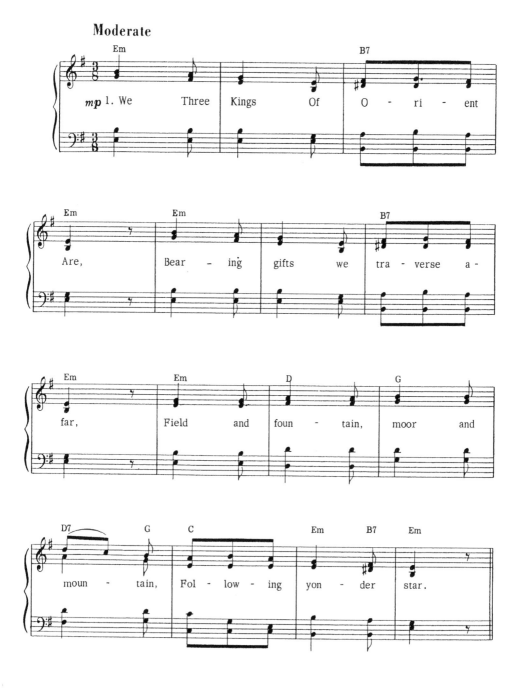

REFRAIN

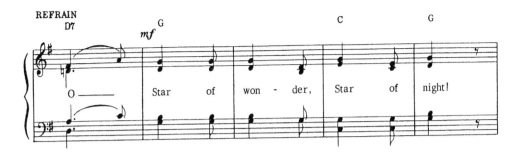

O — Star of won - der, Star of night!

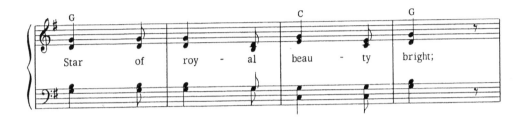

Star of roy - al beau - ty bright;

West - ward lead - ing, Still pro - ceed - ing

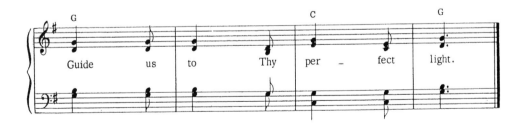

Guide us to Thy per - fect light.

2. Born a King on Bethlehem's plain,
   Gold I bring to crown Him again,
   King forever, ceasing never
   Over us all to reign.
   Refrain

3. Frankincense to offer have I,
   Incense owns a deity nigh:
   Prayer and praising, all men raising,
   Worship Him, God on high.
   Refrain

4. Myrrh is mine; its bitter perfume
   Breathes a life of gathering gloom;
   Sorrowing, sighing, bleeding, dying,
   Sealed in a stone cold tomb.
   Refrain

5. Glorious now behold Him arise,
   King and God, and sacrifice.
   Alleluia, Alleluia!
   Sounds through the earth and skies.
   Refrain

O Come All Ye Faithful

Traditional English carol

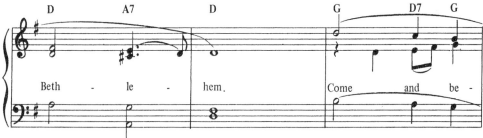

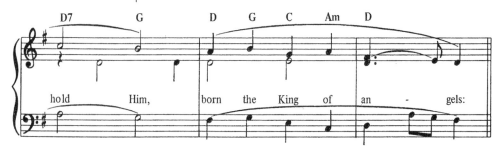

Refrain

O come, let us a - dore Him, O come let us a - dore Him, O come let us a - dore Him, — Christ the —— Lord.

2. Sing, choirs of angels, sing in exultation,
O sing all ye citizens of heaven above!
Glory to God, all Glory in the highest.
Refrain

3. Yea, Lord, we greet Thee, born this happy morning,
Jesus, to Thee be all glory giv'n;
Word of the Father, now in flesh appearing.
Refrain

O Come, O Come Emmanuel

Traditional French carol

Refrain

Re - joice! Re - joice! Em - man - u - el shall come to thee, O Is - ra - el.

2. O come, Thou Wisdom from on high,
And order all things, far and nigh;
To us the path of knowledge show,
And cause us in her ways to go.
Refrain

3. O come, Desire of nations, bind
All peoples in one heart and mind;
Bid envy, strife, and quarrels cease;
Fill the whole world with heaven's peace.
Refrain

4. O come, Thou Day-spring, come and cheer
Our spirits by Thine advent here;
Disperse the gloomy clouds of night,
And death's dark shadows put to flight.
Refrain

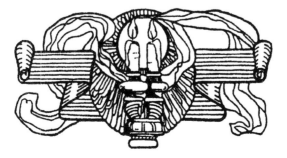

Children, Go Where I Send Thee

Traditional African-American spiritual

3. I'm gonna send thee three by three.
   Three for the Hebrew children.
   Two for Paul and Silas, *etc.*

4. I'm gonna send thee four by four.
   Four for the four that stood at the door.
   Three for the Hebrew children, *etc.*

5. I'm gonna send thee five by five.
   Five for the Gospel preachers.
   Four for the four that stood at the door, *etc.*

6. I'm gonna send thee six by six.
   Six for the six that never got fixed,
   Five for the Gospel preachers, *etc.*

7. I'm gonna send thee seven by seven.
   Seven for the seven that never got to heaven.
   Six for the six that never got fixed, *etc.*

8. I'm gonna send thee eight by eight.
   Eight for the eight that stood at the gate.
   Seven for the seven that never got to heaven, *etc.*

9. I'm gonna send thee nine by nine.
   Nine for the nine all dressed so fine.
   Eight for the eight that stood at the gate, *etc.*

10. I'm gonna send thee ten by ten.
    Ten for the ten commandments.
    Nine for the nine all dressed so fine, *etc.*

Fum, Fum, Fum

Traditional Spanish carol

2. Thanks to God for holidays, sing fum, fum, fum.
   Thanks to God for holidays, sing fum, fum, fum.
   Now we all our voices raise, And sing a song of grateful praise,
   Celebrate in song and story, All the wonders of His glory,
   Fum, fum, fum.

God Rest You Merry, Gentlemen

Traditional English carol

Refrain

O——— ti - dings of com - fort and joy, com-fort and joy,

O——— ti - dings of com - fort and joy.

2. In Bethlehem in Jewry
   This blessèd babe was born
   And laid within a manger
   Upon this blessèd morn;
   The which his mother Mary
   Nothing did take in scorn:
   Refrain

3. From God our heavenly Father
   A blessèd angel came.
   And unto certain shepherds
   Brought tidings of the same,
   How that in Bethlehem was born
   The Son of God by name:
   Refrain

4. "Fear not," then said the angel,
   "Let nothing you affright,
   This day is born a Savior,
   Of virtue, power, and might;
   So frequently to vanquish all
   The friends of Satan quite:"
   Refrain

5. The shepherds at those tidings
   Rejoicèd much in mind,
   And left their flocks a-feeding,
   In tempest, storm, and wind,
   And went to Bethlehem straightway
   This blessèd babe to find:
   Refrain

6. But when to Bethlehem they came,
   Whereat this infant lay
   They found him in a manger,
   Where oxen feed on hay;
   His mother Mary kneeling,
   Unto the Lord did pray:
   Refrain

7. Now to the Lord sing praises,
   All you within this place,
   And with true love and brotherhood
   Each other now embrace;
   This holy tide of Christmas
   All others doth deface:
   Refrain

I Saw Three Ships

Traditional English carol

3. Our Savior Christ and his lady,
   On Christmas Day, on Christmas Day,
   Our Savior Christ and his lady,
   On Christmas Day in the morning.

4. Pray, whither sailed those ships all three? *etc.*

5. O, they sailed into Bethlehem,

6. And all the bells on earth shall ring,

7. And all the angels in heav'n shall sing,

8. And all the souls on earth shall sing,

9. Then let us all rejoice amain!

Good Christian Men, Rejoice

Traditional German carol

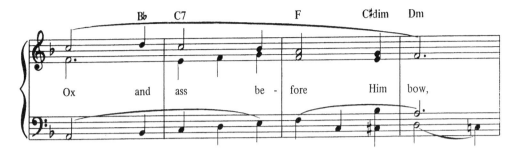

Ox and ass before Him bow,

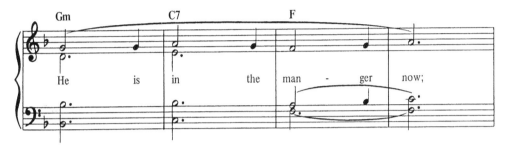

He is in the man - ger now;

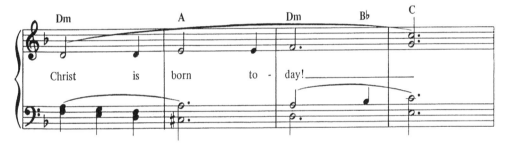

Christ is born to - day!____

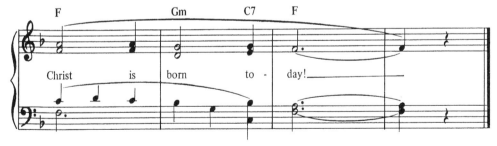

Christ is born to - day!____

2. Good Christian men, rejoice,
   With heart and soul and voice;
   Now ye hear of endless bliss; Joy! Joy!
   Jesus Christ was born for this!
   He hath op'n'd the heavenly door,
   And man is blessèd evermore.
   Christ was born for this,
   Christ was born for this!

3. Good Christian men, rejoice,
   With heart and soul and voice;
   Now ye need not fear the grave; Peace! Peace!
   Jesus Christ was born to save!
   Calls you one and calls you all,
   To gain his everlasting hall.
   Christ was born to save,
   Christ was born to save!

Go Tell It on the Mountain

Traditional African-American spiritual

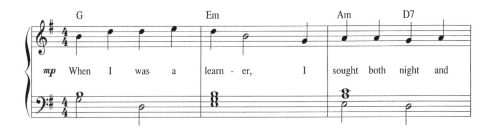

mp When I was a learn - er, I sought both night and

day. I asked the Lord to help me and

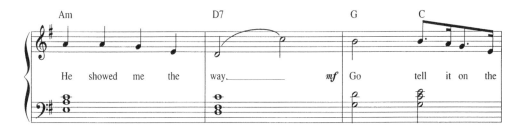

He showed me the way.___ *mf* Go tell it on the

moun - tain, o - ver the hills and

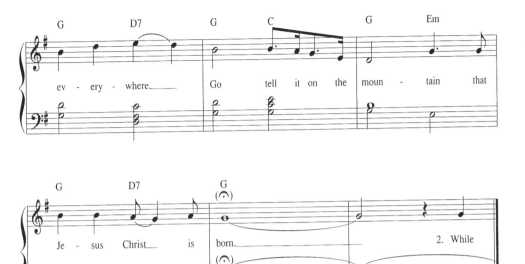

ev - ery - where.___ Go tell it on the moun - tain that

Je - sus Christ___ is born.___ 2. While

2. While shepherds kept their watching,
  O'er wand'ring flock by night;
  Behold! from out of heaven,
  There shown a holy light.
    Refrain

3. And lo, when they had seen it,
  They all bowed down and prayed;
  Then they travelled on together,
  To where the Babe was laid.
    Refrain

4. He made me a watchman,
  Upon the city wall,
  And if I am a Christian
  I am the least of all.
    Refrain

Jingle Bells

Words and music by James S. Pierpont
(1822–1893)

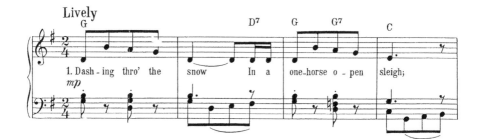

1. Dash - ing thro' the snow In a one-horse o - pen sleigh;

O'er the fields we go, Laugh - ing all the way.

Bells on bob - tail ring, Mak - ing spir - its bright, What

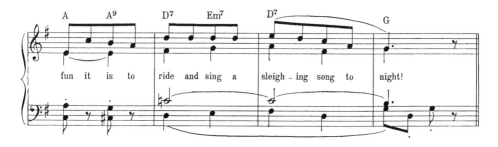

fun it is to ride and sing a sleigh - ing song to night!

REFRAIN

Jin - gle bells! Jin - gle bells! Jin - gle all the

way! Oh, what fun it is to ride In a

one - horse o - pen sleigh. Oh, one - horse o - pen sleigh!

2. A day or two ago
   I thought I'd take a ride,
   Soon Miss Fanny Bright
   Was seated at my side.
   The horse was lean and lank,
   Misfortune seemed his lot,
   He got into a drifted bank,
   And we, we got upsot!
   Refrain

3. Now the ground is white,
   Go it while you're young!
   Take the girls tonight,
   And sing this sleighing song.
   Just get a bobtailed bay,
   Two-forty for his speed,
   Then hitch him to an open sleigh
   And crack! you'll take the lead.
   Refrain

I Heard the Bells on Christmas Day

Words by Henry Wadsworth Longfellow
(1807–1882)

Music by John Baptiste Calkin
(1827–1905)

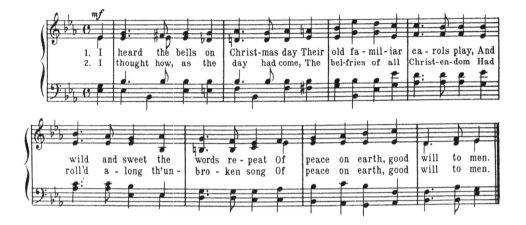

1. I heard the bells on Christmas day Their old fa - mil - iar ca - rols play, And
2. I thought how, as the day had come, The bel-fries of all Christ-en-dom Had

wild and sweet the words re - peat Of peace on earth, good will to men.
roll'd a - long th'un - bro - ken song Of peace on earth, good will to men.

3. Till, ringing, swinging on its way,
The world revolved from night to day,
A voice, a chime, a chant sublime
Of peace on earth, good will to men.

4. Then from each black, accursèd mouth
The cannon thundered in the South,
And with the sound, the carols drowned
Of peace on earth, good will to men.

5. It was as if an earthquake rent
The hearth-stones of a continent,
And made forlorn the households born
Of peace on earth, good will to men.

6. And in despair I bowed my head;
"There is no peace on earth," I said;
"For hate is strong, and mocks the song
Of peace on earth, good will to men."

7. Then pealed the bells more loud and deep:
"God is not dead; nor doth He sleep!
The wrong shall fail, the right prevail,
With peace on earth, good will to men."

Pat-a-pan

Traditional French carol

2. When the men of olden days
   To the King of kings gave praise,
   On the fife and drum did play,
      Tu-re-lu-re-lu,
      Pat-a-pat-a-pan,
   On the fife and drum did play,
   So their hearts were glad and gay!

3. God and man today become
   More in tune than fife and drum,
   So be merry while you play,
      Tu-re-lu-re-lu,
      Pat-a-pat-a-pan,
   So be merry while you play,
   Sing and dance this Christmas Day!

He Is Born
(Il est né)

Traditional French carol

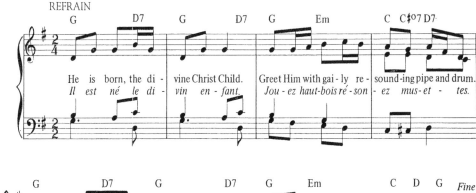

2. *Ah! qu'il est beau, qu'il est charmant,*
   Ah! que ses grâces son parfaites.
   Ah! qu'il est beau, qu'il est charmant,
   Qu'il est doux ce divin enfant.
       Refrain

3. *Une étable est son logement,*
   Un peu de paille est sa couchette,
   Une étable est son logement,
   Pour un Dieu, quel abaissement.
       Refrain

4. *O Jésus, ô roi tout poissant,*
   Tout petit enfant que vous etes,
   O Jésus, ô roi tout poissant,
   Régnez sur nous entièrement.
       Refrain

O Christmas Tree

Traditional German carol

1. O Christ-mas tree, O Christ-mas tree, How true you stand un - chang - ing. O Christ-mas tree, O Christ-mas tree, How true you stand un - chang - ing. Your boughs so green in sum-mer-time, Re - main so green in win-ter-time. O Christ-mas tree, O Christ-mas tree, How true you stand un - chang - ing.

2. O Christmas tree, O Christmas tree,
   Thy message is enduring;
   O Christmas tree, O Christmas tree,
   Thy message is enduring.
   So long ago in Bethlehem
   Was born the Savior of all men;
   O Christmas tree, O Christmas tree,
   Thy message is enduring.

3. O Christmas tree, O Christmas tree,
   Thy faith remains unchanging;
   O Christmas tree, O Christmas tree,
   Thy faith remains unchanging.
   A symbol sent from God above,
   Proclaiming Him the Lord of Love;
   O Christmas tree, O Christmas tree,
   Thy faith remains unchanging!

Deck the Hall

Traditional Welsh carol

Lively

1. Deck the hall with boughs of hol-ly,
   'Tis the sea-son to be jol-ly,
   Fa la la la la la la la la.

Don we now our gay ap-par-el,
Fa la la la la la la la la.

Troll the an-cient Yule-tide car-ol,
Fa la la la la la la la la.

2. See the blazing Yule before us,
   Fa-la-la-la-la, la-la-la-la.
   Strike the harp and join the chorus,
   Fa-la-la-la-la, la-la-la-la.
   Follow me in merry measure,
   Fa-la-la, la-la-la, la-la-la.
   While I tell of Yuletide treasure,
   Fa-la-la-la-la, la-la-la-la.

3. Fast away the old year passes,
   Fa-la-la-la-la, la-la-la-la.
   Hail the new, ye lads and lasses,
   Fa-la-la-la-la, la-la-la-la.
   Sing we joyous all together,
   Fa-la-la, la-la-la, la-la-la.
   Heedless of the wind and weather,
   Fa-la-la-la-la, la-la-la-la.

The Holly and the Ivy

Traditional English carol

3. The holly bears a berry
   As red as any blood,
   And Mary bore sweet Jesus Christ
   To do poor sinners good.
   Refrain

4. The holly bears a prickle
   As sharp as any thorn,
   And Mary bore sweet Jesus Christ
   On Christmas Day in the morn.
   Refrain

5. The holly bears a bark
   As bitter as any gall,
   And Mary bore sweet Jesus Christ
   For to redeem us all.
   Refrain

6. The holly and the ivy,
   Now both are full well grown,
   Of all the trees that are in the wood
   The holly bears the crown.
   Refrain

Christ Was Born on Christmas Day

Words by John M. Neale
(1818–1866)

Traditional German carol

2. He is born to set us free,
   He is born our Lord to be:
   Ex Maria Virgine,
   The God, the Lord, by all adored forever

3. Let the bright red berries glow
   Everywhere in goodly show:
   Christus natus hodie,
   The Babe, the Son, the Holy One of Mary.

4. Christian men, rejoice and sing
   'Tis the birthday of a king:
   Ex Maria Virgine,
   The God, the Lord, by all adored forever.

Lo, How a Rose E'er Blooming

Traditional German carol

The Cherry Tree Carol

Traditional English carol

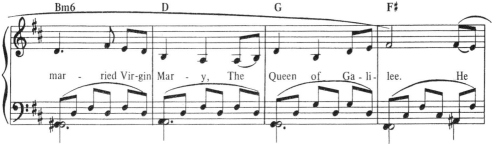

2. When Joseph and Mary walked through an orchard green,
   There were berries and cherries as thick as might be seen,
   There were berries and cherries as thick as might be seen.

3. And Mary spoke to Joseph, so meek and so mild:
   "Joseph, gather me some cherries for I am with child,"
   "Joseph, gather me some cherries for I am with child."

4. And Joseph flew in anger, in anger flew he:
   "Let the father of the baby gather cherries for thee,"
   "Let the father of the baby gather cherries for thee."

5. The up spoke baby Jesus from in Mary's womb:
   "Bend down the tallest tree that my mother might have some,"
   "Bend down the tallest tree that my mother might have some."

6. And bent down the tallest branch till it touchèd Mary's hand,
   Cried she, "Oh, look thou Joseph, I have cherries by command."
   Cried she, "Oh, look thou Joseph, I have cherries by command."

Here We Come A-Wassailing

Traditional English carol

3. We are not daily beggars
   That beg from door to door,
   But we are neighbors' children
   Whom you have seen before:
   Refrain

4. Call up the butler of this house
   Put on his golden ring;
   Let him bring us up a glass of beer
   And better we shall sing:
   Refrain

5. We have got a little purse
   Of stretching leather skin;
   We want a little of your money
   To line it well within:
   Refrain

6. Bring us out a table
   And spread it with a cloth;
   Bring us out a mouldy cheese
   And some of your Christmas loaf;
   Refrain

7. God bless the master of this house
   God bless the mistress too;
   And all the little children
   That round the table go:
   Refrain

8. Good master and good mistress
   While you're sitting by the fire,
   Pray think of us poor children
   Who are wandering in the mire:
   Refrain

Masters in This Hall

Words by William Morris
(1834–1896)

Traditional French tune

Majestically

1. Mas - ters in this hall,____ Hear ye news to- day,

Brought from o - ver- sea, And ev - er I you pray:

Refrain

Now - ell, Now - ell, Now - ell! Now - ell sing we
Now - ell sing we

clear! Holp - en are all folk on earth____ born____
loud! God to - day hath all folk raised____ and____

is God's Son so dear; cast a-down the proud.

2. Then to Bethl'em town
   We went two and two;
   In a sorry place
   We heard the oxen low:
   Refrain

3. Ox and ass Him know,
   Kneeling on their knee,
   Wond'rous joy had I
   This little babe to see:
   Refrain

Christmas Is Coming

Traditional English round

Moderately

Christ - mas is com - ing! The goose is get - ting fat;

Please to put a pen - ny in an old man's —— hat,

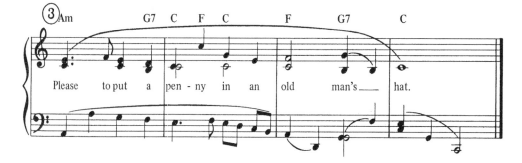

Please to put a pen - ny in an old man's —— hat.

If you have no penny,
A ha'penny will do,
If you have no ha'penny
Then God bless you,
If you have no ha'penny
Then God bless you.

The Boar's Head Carol

Traditional English carol

2. The boar's head as I understand
Is the bravest dish in all the land,
When thus bedecked with a gay garland
Let us *servire cantico.*
(Let us now serve it with a song.)
Refrain

3. Our steward hath provided this
In honor of the King of Bliss,
Which on this day to be servèd is,
In reginensi atrio.
(All within this royal hall.)
Refrain

We Wish You a Merry Christmas

Traditional English carol

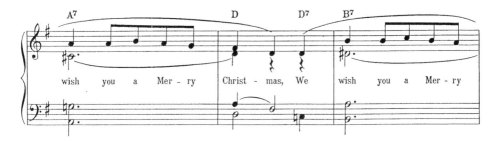

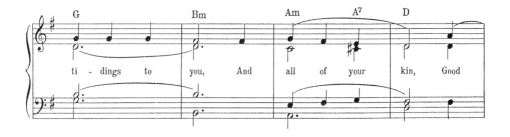

ti - dings   for   Christ - mas   And a   hap - py   New   Year.

2. Oh, bring us some figgy pudding,
   Oh, bring us some figgy pudding,
   Oh, bring us some figgy pudding,
   And bring it right here!
   Refrain

3. We won't go until we get some,
   We won't go until we get some,
   We won't go until we get some,
   So bring it right here.
   Refrain

4. For we all like figgy pudding,
   We all like figgy pudding,
   We all like figgy pudding,
   So bring it right here.
   Refrain

Good King Wenceslas

Words by John M. Neale
(1818–1866)

Traditional Swedish melody

1. Good King Wen - ces - las looked out, on the feast of Ste - phen, when the snow lay round a - bout, deep and crisp and ev - en. Bright - ly shone the moon that night, though the frost was

2. 'Hith - er, page and stand by me, if thou know'st it, tel - ling. Yon - der pea - sant who is he? Where, and what his dwell - ing?' 'Sire, he lives a good league hence, un - der - neath the

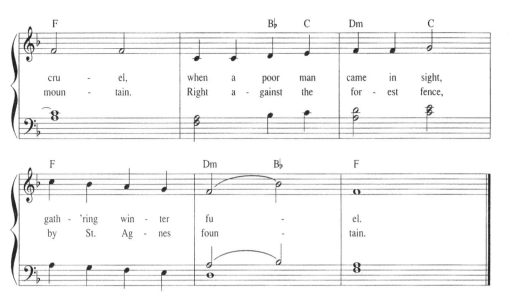

cru - el,
moun - tain.

when a poor man came in sight,
Right a - gainst the for - est fence,

gath - 'ring win - ter fu - el.
by St. Ag - nes foun - tain.

3. "Bring me flesh, and bring me wine,
Bring me pinelogs hither;
Thou and I shall see him dine
When we bear them thither."
Page and monarch forth they went,
Forth they went together:
Through the rude wind's wild lament
And the bitter weather.

4. "Sire, the night is darker now,
And the wind blows stronger;
Fails my heart, I know not how,
I can go no longer."
"Mark my footsteps good, my page;
Tread thou in them boldly.
Thou shalt find the winter's rage
Freeze thy blood less coldly."

5. In his master's steps he trod,
Where the snow lay dinted;
Heat was in the very sod
Which the saint had printed.
Therefore, Christian men be sure,
Wealth or rank possesing,
Ye who now will bless the poor,
Shall youselves find blessing.

The Twelve Days of Christmas

Traditional English carol

Two tur-tle doves and a par-tridge_ in a pear tree. 4. On the

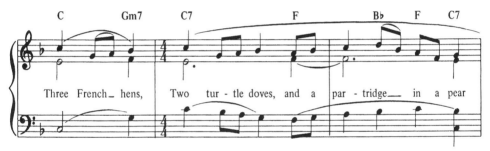

fourth day of Christ-mas my true love gave to me Four call-ing birds,

Three French_ hens, Two tur-tle doves, and a par-tridge_ in a pear

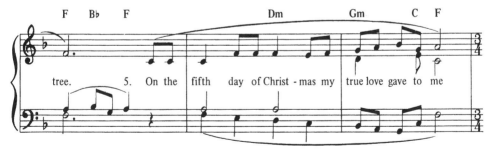

tree. 5. On the fifth day of Christ-mas my true love gave to me

Five gold-en rings, Four_ call-ing birds, Three French hens,

G7 C F B♭ F C7 F B♭ F

Two — tur - tle doves, and a par - tridge — in a pear tree.

F Dm C F C Gm7

6. On the sixth day of Christ - mas my true love gave to me Six geese a - lay - ing,
7. On the seventh day of Christ - mas my true love gave to me Sev - en swans a - swim-ming,
8. On the eighth day of Christ - mas my true love gave to me Eight maids a - milk-ing,
9. On the ninth day of Christ - mas my true love gave to me Nine la - dies wait-ing,
10. On the tenth day of Christ - mas my true love gave to me Ten lords a - leap-ing,
11. On the eleventh day of Christ - mas my true love gave to me 'Lev-en pip - ers pip - ing,
12. On the twelfth day of Christ - mas my true love gave to me Twelve drum-mers drum-ming,

Am Dm G7 C F Dm Gm Dm

Five gold - en rings, Four — call - ing birds, Three French hens,

G7 C F B♭ F C7 | **6,7,8,9,10,11.** F B♭ F | **12.** F B♭ F

Two — tur - tle doves, and a par - tridge — in a pear tree. | tree.

D.S. *rit.*

* *Repeat this measure as often as necessary to sing the accumulated lyrics of all previous verses, each time ending with "Six geese a-laying."*